On a Grass-Green Horn

On a

Grass-Green Horn

Old Scotch and English Ballads

Drawings by **Ati Forberg**

Atheneum *New York*
1965

Drawings copyright © 1965 by Ati Forberg
All rights reserved
Library of Congress catalog card number 65-21715
Published simultaneously in Canada by McClelland & Stewart Ltd.
Manufactured in the United States of America
Printed by Halliday Lithograph Corporation,
  West Hanover, Massachusetts
Bound by H. Wolff, New York
First Edition

for Fanny

Contents

Introduction

The ballads in this book have no individual authors. They are legends of the people of England, Ireland, and Scotland of the Middle Ages, passed on by word of mouth. Since few in those times could read, write, or travel, people relied on wandering minstrels to bring news, songs, and stories. The minstrels took much of their material from stories they had heard, fragments of which were sometimes so old they reached back toward pre-history and the celtic Druids. Preserved in some of these ballads was a sense of magic, shape-changing, and a feeling about the land unlike any we have now.

With the advent of modern printing and communication, the voices of the minstrels and the people telling the old tales gradually grew still. But the ballads and poetry began to be set down in writing in the 17th century, and there are now many versions of some of them, recorded by many different collectors.

On a Grass-Green Horn

"And thrice she blew on a grass-green horn ..."

Alison Gross

Thomas Rymer

True Thomas lay o'er yon grassy bank,
And he beheld a lady gay,
A lady that was brisk and bold,
Come riding o'er the ferny brae.[1]

Her skirt was of the grass-green silk,
Her mantel of the velvet fine,
At every lock o' her horse's mane
Hung fifty silver bells and nine.

1. brae—*a hillside*

True Thomas he took off his hat,
And bowed him low down till his knee:
"All hail, thou mighty Queen of Heaven!
For your peer on earth I never did see."

"O no, O no, True Thomas," she says,
"That name does not belong to me;
I am but the queen of fair Elfland,
And I'm come here for to visit thee.

"But ye maun² go wi' me now, Thomas,
True Thomas, you maun go wi' me,
For ye maun serve me seven years,
Thro weal or woe as may chance to be."

She turned about her milk-white steed,
And took True Thomas up behind,
And aye³ whene'er her bridle rang,
The steed flew swifter than the wind.

For forty days and forty nights
He wade thro red blude to the knee,
And he saw neither sun nor moon,
But heard the roaring of the sea.

O they rode on, and further on,
Until they came to a garden green:
"Light down, light down, ye lady free,
Some of that fruit let me pull to thee."

2. maun—*must*   3. aye—*always*

"O no, O no, True Thomas," she says,
"That fruit maun not be touched by thee,
 For a' the plagues that are in hell
 Light on the fruit of this country.

"But I have a loaf here in my lap,
 And likewise a bottle of claret wine,
 And now ere we go farther on,
 We'll rest a while, and ye may dine."

When he had eaten and drunk his fill:
"Lay down your head upon my knee,"
 The lady said, "ere we climb yon hill
 And I will show you ferlys [4] three.

"O see not ye yon narrow road,
 So thick beset wi' thorns and briers?
 That is the path of righteousness,
 Tho after it but few enquires.

"And see not ye that broad broad road,
 That lies across yon lilly leven? [5]
 That is the path of wickedness,
 Tho some call it the road to heaven.

"And see not ye that bonny road,
 Which winds about the ferny brae?
 That is the road to fair Elfland,
 Where you and I this night maun gae.

4. ferlys—*wonders*   5. leven—*glade*   5

"But Thomas, ye maun hold your tongue,
Whatever you may hear or see,
For gin ae [6] word you should chance to speak,
You will ne'er get back to your own country."

He has gotten a coat of the even cloth,
And a pair of shoes of velvet green,
And till seven years were past and gone
True Thomas on earth was never seen.

6. gin ae—*if one*

Lord Randal

"O where hae ye been, Lord Randal, my son?
  O where hae ye been, my handsome young man?"
"I hae been to the wild wood; mother, make my bed soon,
  For I'm weary wi' hunting, and fain [1] would lie doon."

"Where gat ye your dinner, Lord Randal, my son?
  Where gat ye your dinner, my handsome young man?"
"I dined wi' my true love; mother, make my bed soon,
  For I'm weary wi' hunting, and fain would lie doon."

"What gat ye to your dinner, Lord Randal, my son?
  What gat ye to your dinner, my handsome young man?"
"I gat eels boil'd in broo'; [2] mother, make my bed soon,
  For I'm weary wi' hunting, and fain would lie doon."

"What became of your bloodhounds, Lord Randal, my son?
  What became of your bloodhounds, my handsome young
      man?"
"O they swell'd and they died; mother, make my bed soon,
  For I'm weary wi' hunting, and fain would lie doon."

"O I fear ye are poison'd, Lord Randal, my son!
  O I fear ye are poison'd, my handsome young man!"
"O yes! I am poison'd; mother, make my bed soon,
  For I'm sick at the heart, and I fain would lie doon."

1. fain—*with joy*   2. broo'—*broth, juice*   7

Broom, Green Broom

There was an old man lived out in the wood,
His trade was a-cutting of Broom,[1] green Broom;
He had but one son without thrift, without good,
Who lay in his bed till 'twas noon, bright noon.

The old man awoke one morning and spoke,
He swore he would fire the room, that room,
If his John would not rise and open his eyes,
And away to the wood to cut Broom, green Broom.

1. Broom—*a shrub*

So Johnny arose, and he slipped on his clothes,
And away to the wood to cut Broom, green Broom.
He sharpened his knives for once he contrives
To cut a great bundle of Broom, green Broom.

When Johnny passed under a lady's fine house,
Passed under a lady's fine room, fine room,
She called to her maid, "Go fetch me," she said,
"Go fetch me the boy that sells Broom, green Broom."

When Johnny came in to the lady's fine house,
And stood in the lady's fine room, fine room;
"Young Johnny," she said, "Will you give up your trade,
And marry a lady in bloom, full bloom?"

Johnny gave his consent, and to church they both went,
And he wedded the lady in bloom, full bloom.
At market and fair, all folks do declare,
There is none like the Boy that sold Broom, green Broom.   *9*

The Golden Vanity

"A ship I have got in the North Country
And she goes by the name of the Golden Vanity,
O I fear she'll be taken by a Spanish Ga-la-lee,
As she sails by the Low-lands low."

To the Captain then up spake the little Cabin-boy,
He said, "What is my fee, if the galley I destroy?
The Spanish Ga-la-lee, if no more it shall annoy,
As you sail by the Low-lands low."

"Of silver and of gold I will give to you a store;
  And my pretty little daughter that dwelleth on the shore,
  Of treasure and of fee as well, I'll give to thee galore,
  As we sail by the Low-lands low."

Then they row'd him tight in a black bull's skin,
  And he held all in his hand an augur sharp and thin,
  And he swam until he came to the Spanish Gal-la-lin,
  As she lay by the Low-lands low.

He bored with his augur, he bored once and twice,
  And some were playing cards, and some were playing dice,
  When the water flowed in it dazzled their eyes,
  And she sank by the Low-lands low.

So the Cabin-boy did swim all to the larboard side,
  Saying, "Captain! take me in, I am drifting with the tide!"
  "I will shoot you! I will kill you!" the cruel Captain cried,
  "You may sink by the Low-lands low."

Then the Cabin-boy did swim all to the starboard side,
  Saying, "Messmates, take me in, I am drifting with the tide!"
  Then they laid him on the deck, and he closed his eyes and
      died,
  As they sailed by the Low-lands low.

They sew'd his body tight in an old cow's hide,
  And they cast the gallant Cabin-boy out over the ship side,
  And left him without more ado to drift with the tide,
  And to sink by the Low-lands low.

Tammie Doodle

Tammie Doodle was a cantie[1] chiel[2]
Fu' cantie and fu' crouse[3]
The fairy like him unco[4] weel,
And built him a wee house.

And when the house was all built up
And finished but the door
A fairy it came skipping in
And danced upon the floor.

The fairy it whirled up and down
It loupit[5] and it flang,[6]
It friskit[7] and it whiskit[8] roun'
And croon'd a fairy song.

At length it whistled loud and shrill
And in came all the gang.
Till poor little Tammie Doodle
Was most smothered in the thrang.

1. cantie—*cheerful, lively*
2. chiel—*a young man*
3. crouse—*cocky, lively*
4. unco—*uncommonly, extremely*
5. loupit—*leaped*
6. flang—*capered about*
7. frisket—*skipped, danced*
8. whiskit—*moved with a sweeping motion*

Kemp Owyne

Her mother died when she was young,
Which gave her cause to make great moan;
Her father married the worst woman
That ever lived in Christendom.

She served her with foot and hand,
In everything that she could dee;
Till once, in an unlucky time,
She threw her in over Craigy's sea.

Says, "Lie you there, dove Isabel,
And all my sorrows lie with thee;
Till Kemp Owyne come over the sea,
And borrow [1] you with kisses three,
Let all the world do what they will,
Oh borrowed shall you never be."

Her breath grew strong, her hair grew long,
And twisted thrice about the tree,
And all the people, far and near,
Thought that a savage beast was she;
This news did come to Kemp Owyne,
Where he lived far beyond the sea.

He hasted him to Craigy's sea,
And on the savage beast look'd he;
Her breath was strong, her hair was long,
And twisted was about the tree,
And with a swing she came about:
"Come to Craigy's sea, and kiss with me."

1. borrow—*redeem*

"Here is a royal belt," she cried,
"That I have found in the green sea:
    And while your body it is on,
    Drawn shall your blood never be;
    But if you touch me, tail or fin,
    I vow my belt your death shall be."

He stepped in, gave her a kiss,
The royal belt he brought him wi';
    Her breath was strong, her hair was long,
    And twisted twice about the tree,
    And with a swing she came about:
"Come to Craigy's sea, and kiss with me."

"Here is a royal ring," she said,
"That I have found in the green sea;
    And while your finger it is on,
    Drawn shall your blood never be;
    But if you touch me, tail or fin,
    I swear my ring your death shall be."

He stepped in, gave her a kiss,
The royal ring he brought him wi';
    Her breath was strong, her hair was long,
    And twisted once around the tree,
    And with a swing she came about:
"Come to Craigy's sea, and kiss with me."

"Here is a royal brand,"[2] she said,
"That I have found in the green sea;
  And while your body it is on,
  Drawn shall your blood never be;
  But if you touch me, tail or fin,
  I swear my brand your death shall be."

He stepped in, gave her a kiss,
The royal brand he brought him wi';
  Her breath was sweet, her hair grew short,
  And twisted none about the tree;
  And smilingly she came about,
  As fair a woman as fair could be.

2. brand—*sword*

Henry Martyn

In merry Scotland, in merry Scotland
There lived brothers three;
They all did cast lots which of them should go
A-robbing upon the salt sea.

The lot it fell on Henry Martyn,
The youngest of the three;
That he should go rob on the salt, salt sea
To maintain his brothers and he.

He had not a-sailed a long winter's night
Nor yet a short winter's day,
Before that he met with a loftly old ship
Come sailing along that way.

O when she came by Henry Martyn,
"I prithee now, let us go!"
"Oh no! God wot,[1] that, that will I not,
O that will I never do."

"Stand off! stand off!" said Henry Martyn,
"For you shall not pass by me;
For I am a robber all on the salt sea
To maintain us brothers three."

For three long hours they merrily fought,
For hours they fought full three,
At last a deep wound got Henry Martyn
And down by the mast fell he.

'Twas broadside to a broadside[2] then,
And a rain and hail of blows,
And the salt sea ran in, ran in, ran in,
To the bottom then she goes.

Bad news, bad news for old England,
Bad news has come to the town,
For a rich merchant's vessel is cast away,
And all her brave seamen drown.

Bad news, bad news through London street,
Bad news has come to the king,
For all the brave lives of the mariners lost,
That are sunk in the watery main.[3]

1. wot—*knows*
2. broadside—*firing all guns on one side of a ship*
3. main—*the great sea*

Bonny George Campbell

High upon Highlands,
And laigh¹ upon Tay,
Bonny George Campbell
Rode out on a day:
Saddled and bridled,
Sae gallant to see,
Home came his good horse,
But never came he.

Down ran his old mother,
Greetin' full sair;²
Out ran his bonny bride,
Reaving³ her hair;
"My meadow lies green,
And my corn is unshorn,
My barn is to bigg,⁴
And my babe is unborn."

Saddled and bridled
And booted rode he;
A plume in his helmet,
A sword at his knee;
But toom⁵ came his saddle
A' bloody to see,
O home came his good horse,
But never came he!

1. laigh—*a lowland, low*   4. bigg—*build*
2. sair—*sore, sorry*   5. toom—*empty*
3. reaving—*tearing*

Earl Mar's Daughter

It was intill[1] a pleasant time,
Upon a summer's day,
The noble Earl Mar's daughter
Went forth to sport and play.

And while she play'd and sported
Below a green oak tree,
There she saw a sprightly doo[2]
Set on a tower sae hie.

"O Coo-me-doo, my love sae true,
If ye'll come down to me,
Ye'll hae a cage o' good red gold
Instead o' simple tree.

1. intill—*in*   2. doo—*dove*

"I'll put gold hingers³ roun' your cage,
And silver roun' your wa';
I'll gar⁴ ye shine as fair a bird
As any o' them a'."

But she had nae these words well spoke,
Nor yet these words well said,
Till Coo-me-doo flew from the tower
And lighted on her head.

3. hingers—*hangers*   4. gar—*make; compel*

Then she has brought this pretty bird
Home to her bowers and ha',
And made him shine as fair a bird
As any o' them a'.

When day was gone, and night was come,
About the evening-tide,
This lady spied a gallant youth
'Stand straight up by her side.

"From whence came ye, young man?" she said;
"That does surprise me sair; [5]
My door was bolted right secure,
What way hae you come here?"

"O hold your tongue, ye lady fair,
Let a' your folly be;
Mind ye not o' your turtle-doo
Ye wiled from off the tree?"

"What country come ye from?" she said,
"An' what's your pedigree?"
"O it was but this very day
That I came over the sea.

"My mother lives on foreign isles,
A queen o' high degree;
And by her spells I am a doo
With you to live an' dee."

5. sair—*extremely*

"O Coo-me-doo, my love sae true,
  Nae mair from me ye'll gae."
"That's never my intent, my love;
  As ye said, it shall be sae."

Then he stay'd in bower wi' her
For six long years and one,
Till six young sons to him she bare,
And the seventh she's brought home.

But aye,[6] as ever a child was born,
He carried them away,
And brought them to his mother's care
As fast as he could fly.

When he had stay'd in bower wi' her
For seven long years and mair
There came a lord o' high renown
To court this lady fair.

But still his proffer she refused
And a' his presents too;
Says, "I'm content to live alone
Wi' my bird Coo-me-doo."

Her father swore a mighty oath
  Among the nobles all,
"The morn, or ere I eat or drink,
  This bird I will gar kill."

6. aye—*always*

The bird was sitting in his cage
And heard what they did say;
Says, "Wae is me, and you forlorn,
If I do longer stay!"

Then Coo-me-doo took flight and flew
And afar beyond the sea,
And lighted near his mother's castle
On a tower o' gold sae hie.

His mother she was walking out
To see what she could see,
And there she saw her one young son
Set on the tower sae hie.

"Get dancers here to dance," she said,
"And minstrels for to play;
For here's my young son Florentine
Come home wi' me to stay."

"Get nae dancers to dance, mother,
Nor minstrels for to play;
For the mother o' my seven sons,
The morn's her wedding-day."

"O tell me, tell me, Florentine,
Tell me, an tell me true;
Tell me this day without a flaw
What I will do for you?"

"Instead of dancers to dance, mother,
  Or minstrels for to play,
  Turn four-and-twenty well-wight[7] men
  Like storks in feathers gray:

"My seven sons in seven swans
  Above their heads to flee;[8]
  And I mysell a gay goshawk,
  A bird o' high degree."

Then sighing said the Queen hersel',
"That thing's too high for me!"
  But she applied to an old woman
  Who had mair skill than she.

Instead o' dancers to dance a dance,
  Or minstrels for to play,
  Four-and-twenty well-wight men
  Turn'd birds o' feathers gray.

Her seven sons in seven swans,
  Above their heads to flee;
  And he himsel' a gay goshawk,
  A bird o' high degree.

This flock o' birds took flight and flew
  Beyond the raging sea,
  And landed near the Earl Mar's castle,
  Took shelter in every tree.

7. wight—*strong*   8. flee—*fly*

They were a flock o' pretty birds
Right comely to be seen;
The people view'd them wi' surprise
As they danced on the green.

These birds flew out from every tree
And lighted on the ha',
And from the roof with force did flee
Among the nobles a'.

The storks there seized ilk [9] wedding-guest
They could not fight nor flee;
The swans they bound the bridegroom fast
Below a green oak tree.

They lighted next on the bride-maidens,
Then on the bride's own head;
And wi' the twinkling o' an ee
The bride an' them were fled.

There's ancient men at weddings been
For sixty years or more.
But siccan [10] a curious wedding-day
They never saw before.

For naething could the company do,
Nor naething could they say;
But they saw a flock o' pretty birds
That took their bride away.

9. ilk—*each, every*   10. siccan—*such*

The Wee Wee Man

As I was walking all alone,
Atween a water and a wa',
And there I spied a wee wee man,
He was the least that ere I saw.

His legs were scarce a shathmont's[1] length,
And thick and thimber[2] was his thigh;
Between his brows there was a span,[3]
And between his shoulders there was three.

1. shathmont—*6 inches*   3. span—*9 inches*
2. thimber—*massive*

He took up a mickle [4] stone,
And he flang't as far as I could see;
Though I had been a Wallace wight, [5]
I couldna liften't to my knee.

"O wee wee man, but ye be strong!
 Oh, tell me where thy dwelling be?"
"My dwelling's down at yon bonny bower,
 O will ye go with me and see?"

On we lept, and awa' we rode,
Till we came to yon bonny green;
We lighted down for to feed our horse
And out there came a lady sheen; [6]

Wi' four and twenty at her back
All comely clad in glisterin' green;
Though the King o' Scotland had been there,
The warst o' them might hae been his queen.

On we lept, and awa' we rode,
Til we come to yon bonny ha';
Where the roof was o' the beaten gold,
And the floor was o' the crystal a'.

When we came to the stair foot
Ladies were dancing, jimp [7] and sma';
But in the twinkling of an eye,
My wee wee man was clean awa'.

4. mickle—*great*
5. Wallace wight—*hero strong*
6. sheen—*shining*
7. jimp—*slender*

Young Waters

About Yule, when the wind blew cool;
And the round tables began,
A' there is come to our king's court
Many a well-favored man.

The queen looked o'er the castle wa',
Beheld both dale and down,
And then she saw young Waters
Come riding to the town.

His footmen they did run before,
His horsemen rode behind;
One mantle of the burning gold
Did keep him from the wind.

Golden girthed his horse before,
And silver shod behind;
The horse young Waters rode upon
Was fleeter then the wind.

Out then spake a wily lord,
Unto the queen said he:
"O tell me what's the fairest face
Rides in the company?"

"I've seen lord, and I've seen laird,[1]
And knights of high degree,
But a fairer face than young Waters
Mine eye did never see."

Out then spake the jealous king
And an angry man was he:
"O if he had been twice as fair,
You might have excepted me."

"You'r neither laird nor lord," she says,
"But the king that wears the crown;
There is not a knight in fair Scotland,
But to thee maun[2] bow down."

1. laird—*a landowner*   2. maun—*must*

For a' that she could do or say,
Appeased he would nae be;
But for the words which she had said,
Young Waters he maun dee.

They hae ta'en young Waters,
And put fetters to his feet;
They hae ta'en young Waters,
And thrown him in dungeon deep.

"Oft I have ridden thro' Stirling town,
In the wind but and[3] the weet;
But I ne'er rode thro' Stirling town
Wi' fetters at my feet.

"Oft have I ridden thro' Stirling town,
In the wind but and the rain;
But I ne'er rode thro' Stirling town
Ne'er to return again."

They had ta'en to the heading[4]-hill
His young son in his cradle;
And they hae ta'en to the heading-hill
His horse but and his saddle.

They hae ta'en to the heading-hill
His lady fair to see;
And for the words the queen had spoke
Young Waters he did dee.

3. but and—*and also*   4. heading—*beheading*   *33*

The Three Ravens

There were three ravens sat on a tree,
They were as black as they might be.

The one of them said to his mate,
"Where shall we our breakfast take?"

"Down in yonder green field
There lies a knight slain under his shield;

"His hounds they lie down at his feet,
So well do they their master keep;

"His hawks they fly so eagerly
  There's no fowl dare come him nigh.

"Down there comes a fallow doe
  As great with young as she might goe.

"She lift up his bloody head
  And kiss'd his wounds that were so red.

"She got him up upon her back
  And carried him to earthen lake.

"She buried him before the prime,[1]
  She was dead herself ere evensong time.

"God send every gentleman
  Such hounds, such hawks, and such a leman!"[2]

1. prime—*dawn*   2. leman—*lover*   *35*

Alison Gross

O Alison Gross, that lives in yon tow'r
The ugliest witch in the north countrie,
She trysted [1] me one day up till her bow'r
And many fair speeches she made to me.

She strok'd my head, and she comb'd my hair,
And she set me down softly on her knee;
Says—"If you will be my leman [2] sae true,
Sae many braw [3] things as I will you gie."

1. trysted—*invited*   3. braw—*good, fine*
2. leman—*lover*

She show'd me a mantle of red scarlet,
With golden flowers and fringes fine;
Says—"If ye will be my leman sae true,
This goodly gift it shall be thine."

"Awa', awa', ye ugly witch,
  Hold far awa', and let me be!
I never will be your leman sae true,
  And I wish I were out o' your company."

She neist brought a sark⁴ o' the softest silk,
Well wrought wi' pearls about the band;
Says—"Gin⁵ ye will be my own true love,
This goodly gift ye shall command."

She show'd me a cup o' the good red gold,
Weel set in jewels sae fair to see;
Says—"Gin ye will be my leman sae true,
This goodly gift I will ye gie."

"Awa', awa', ye ugly witch,
  Hold far awa', and let me be!
For I wadna once kiss your ugly mouth
  For a' the gifts that you could gie."

She's turned her right and round about
And thrice she blew on a grass-green horn;
And she sware by the moon and the stars above
That she'd gar⁶ me rue the day I was born.

4. sark—*shirt*   5. gin—*if*   6. gar—*make, compel*

Then out has she ta'en a silver wand,
And she's turned her three times round and round;
She's mutter'd sic words that my strength it fail'd,
And I fell down senseless on the ground.

She turned me into an ugly worm,[7]
And gar'd me twine about the tree;
And aye[8] on ilka[9] Saturday's night
Alison Gross she came to me;

Wi' silver basin and silver comb,
To comb my headie upon her knee;
But ere that I'd kiss her ugly mouth,
I'd sooner gae twining around the tree.

But as it fell out, on last Hallowe'en
When the Seely Court[10] came ridin' by,
The Queen lighted down on a flowery bank,
Close by the tree where I wont to lie.

She took me up in her milkwhite hand,
She stroked me three times o'er her knee;
She changed me back to my proper shape,
And nae more do I twine about the tree.

7. worm—*snake*   9. ilka—*every*
8. aye—*always*   10. Seely Court—*fairies*

The Mermaid

To yon false stream that, near the sea,
Hides many an elf and plum,
And rives[1] with fearful din the stones,
A witless knight did come.

The day shines clear—far in he's gone,
Where shells are silver bright;
Fishes were louping[2] all aroun',
And sparkling to the light.

When, as he laved,[3] sounds came sae sweet
From every rock and tree;
The spell was out, 'twas him it doom'd
The mermaid's face to see.

From 'neath a rock, soon, soon she rose,
And stately on she swam,
Stopp'd in the midst, and beck'd and sang
To him to stretch his han'.

1. rives—*tears apart*   3. laved—*washed*
2. louping—*leaping*

Golden glist[4] the yellow links
That round her neck she'd twine;
Her eyes were of the skyie blue,
Her lips did mock the wine.

The smile upon her bonnie cheek
Was sweeter than the bee;
Her voice excell'd the birdie's song
Upon the birchen tree.

Sae couthie,[5] couthie did she look,
And meikle[6] had she fleech'd;[7]
Out shot his hand—alas! alas!
Fast in the swirl he screech'd.

The mermaid laughed, her spell was gone,
And kelpie's[8] blast[9] was blowing;
Full low she dook'd,[10] ne'er raise again,
For deep, deep was the fawing.[11]

Above the stream his wraith was seen,
Warlocks[12] twirled long at gloaming;
That e'en was coarse, the blast blew hoarse,
Ee long the waves were foaming.

4. glist—*glistened*
5. couthie—*kindly*
6. meikle—*much*
7. fleech'd—*flattered wheedled*
8. kelpie—*a water sprite associated with drownings*
9. blast—*a burst of breath*
10. dook'd—*plunged*
11. fawing—*falling*
12. Warlocks—*male witches*

Three Knights from Spain

We are three Brethren come from Spain,
All in French garlands;
We are come to court your daughter Jane,
And adieu to you, my darlings.

My daughter Jane!—she is too young,
All in French garlands;
She cannot bide your flattering tongue,
And adieu to you, my darlings.

Be she young, or be she old,
All in French garlands;
'Tis for a bride she must be sold,
And adieu to you, my darlings.

A bride, a bride, she shall not be,
All in French garlands;
Till she go though this world with me,
And adieu to you, my darlings.

Then shall you keep your daughter Jane,
All in French garlands;
Come once, we come not here again,
And adieu to you, my darlings.

Turn back, turn back, you Spanish Knights,
All in French garlands;
Scour, scour your spurs, till they be bright,
And adieu to you, my darlings.

Sharp shine our spurs, all richly wrought,
All in French garlands;
In towns afar our spurs were bought
And adieu to you, my darlings.

Smell my lilies, smell my roses,
All in French garlands;
Which of my maidens do you choose?
And adieu to you, my darlings.

Not she. Not she. Thy youngest, Jane!
All in French garlands;
We ride—and ride not back again,
And adieu to you, my darlings.

In every pocket a thousand pound,
All in French garlands;
On every finger a gay gold ring,
And adieu to you, my darlings,
And adieu to you, my darlings.

The Demon Lover

"O where have you been, my long, long love,
  This long seven years and more?"
"O I'm come to seek my former vows
  Ye granted me before."

"O hold your tongue of your former vows,
  For they will breed sad strife;
  O hold your tongue of your former vows,
  For I am become a wife."

He turn'd him right and round about,
And the tear blinded his ee;
"I wad never hae trodden on Irish ground,
If it had not been for thee.

"I might hae had a king's daughter,
Far, far beyond the sea;
I might have had a king's daughter,
Had it not been for love o' thee."

"If you might have had a king's daughter,
Yer sel ye had to blame;
Ye might have taken the king's daughter,
For ye kenned [1] that I was nane. [2]

"If I was to leave my husband dear,
And my two babes also,
O what have you to take me to,
If with you I should go?"

"I hae seven ships upon the sea,
The eighth brought me to land;
With four and twenty bold mariners,
And music on every hand."

She has taken up her two little babes,
Kiss'd them both cheek and chin;
"O fare ye well, my own two babes,
For I'll never see you again."

1. kenned—*know*   2. nane—*none*

She set her foot upon the ship,
No mariners could she behold;
But the sails were o' the taffety,
And the masts o' the beaten gold.

She had not sail'd a league,[3] a league,
A league but barely three,
When dismal grew his countenance
And drumlie[4] grew his ee.

They had not sailed a league, a league,
A league but barely three,
Until she espied his cloven foot,
And she wept right bitterly.

3. league—*about three miles*   4. drumlie—*gloomy*   47

"O hold your tongue of your weeping," says he,
"Of your weeping now let me be;
   I will show you how the lilies grow
   On the banks of Italy."

"O what hills are yon, yon pleasant hills,
   That the sun shines sweetly on?"
"O yon are the hills of heaven," he said,
"Where you will never win."

"O whaten a mountain is yon," she said,
"All so dreary wi' frost and snow?"
"O yon is the mountain of hell," he cried,
"Where you and I will go."

   He struck the top-mast wi' his hand,
   The fore-mast wi' his knee;
   And he brake that gallant ship in twain,
   And sank her in the sea.

Get Up and Bar the Door

It fell about the Martinmas[1] time,
And a gay time it was then,
When our goodwife got puddings to make,
And she's boil'd them in the pan.

The wind sae cold blew south and north,
And blew into the floor;
Quoth our goodman to our goodwife,
"Gae out and bar the door."

"My hand is in my hussyfskap,
Goodman, as ye may see;
An' it shouldna be barr'd this hundred year,
It's no be barr'd for me."

They made a paction[2] 'tween them two,
They made it firm and sure,
That the first word who'er should speak
Should rise and bar the door.

Then by there came two gentlemen,
At twelve o'clock at night,
And they could neither see house nor hall,
Nor coal nor candle-light.

1. Martinmas time—*early November*
2. paction—*an agreement*

"Now whether is this a rich man's house,
  Or whether is it a poor?"
But ne'er a word would one o' them speak,
  For barring of the door.

And first they ate the white puddings,
  And then they ate the black.
Tho' muckle[3] thought the goodwife to hersel'
  Yet ne'er a word she spake.

Then said the one unto the other,
"Here, man, take ye my knife;
  Do ye take off the old man's beard,
  And I'll kiss the goodwife."

"But there's no water in the house,
  And what shall we do then?"
"What ails ye at the pudding-broo,[4]
  That boils into the pan?"

O up then started our goodman,
  An angry man was he:
"Will ye kiss my wife before my eye
  And scald me wi' pudding-bree?"

Then up and started our goodwife,
  Gied three skips on the floor:
"Goodman, you've spoken the foremost word!
  Get up and bar the door."

3. muckle—*much*   4. broo, bree—*broth*

The Lowlands O' Holland

"The love that I hae chosen,
  I'll therewith be content
  The salt sea shall be frozen
  Before that I repent.
  Repent it shall I never
  Until the day I dee;
  But the Lowlands of Holland
  Hae twinn'd[1] my love and me.

1. twinn'd—*parted*

My love he built a bonny ship
And set her to the main,[2]
Wi' twenty-four brave mariners
To sail her out and hame.
But the weary wind began to rise
The sea began to rout
And my love and his bonny ship
Turned withershins[3] about.

There shall nae mantle[4] cross my back
No comb gae in my hair
Neither shall coal nor candlelight
Shine in my mower mair,[5]
Nor shall I choose another love
Until the day I dee
Since the Lowlands o' Holland
Hae twinn'd my love and me."

"Now hold your tongue, my daughter dear,
Be still, and bide content,
There's other lads in Galloween
Ye needna sair[6] lament."
"Oh there is none at a' for me,
I never loved a lad but one
And he's drowned in the sea."

2. main—*high seas*
3. withershins—*contrariwise*
4. mantle—*a widow's cloak*
5. mair—*more*
6. sair—*sore*